PIANO

Adventures® *by Nancy and Randall Faber*

THE BASIC PIANO METHOD

This book belongs to: _____

Production Coordinator: Jon Ophoff
Cover and Illustrations: Terpstra Design, San Francisco
Engraving: Dovetree Productions, Inc.

ISBN 978-1-61677-648-0

Progress Chart

Keep track of your progress.
Colour or put a star sticker for each item.

About Technique & Performance
Overview for Teachers and Parents

Technique at the piano requires more than finger muscles. Piano technique involves sophisticated coordination between the body, arm, wrist, and finger. We call these motions "technique gestures."

In this series, advanced techniques are prepared at the early levels by using appropriate sequencing and effective presentation. In fact, it is important to address technical gesture early on, because bad habits are difficult to remedy after years of practise.

At each level of Piano Adventures® the student is introduced to level-appropriate "Technique Secrets" that promote fluent playing while preventing bad habits. These secrets are used as daily warm-ups for the exercises that follow in the book. This combination of warm-ups, exercises, and etudes ensures correct practise and smart repetition.

Performance at the piano requires technical control of touch and sound. Artistry is the goal of performance, and technique is the means to artistry.

The Piano Adventures® Technique & Performance series brings together technique and artistry by including an etude and performance piece with each unit. These pieces are specially written to bring out musical expression at the keyboard using the specific techniques being learned.

Great technique is developed through observant repetition. Effective practise includes understanding the mechanics of piano technique to ensure that repetitions are fluent and accurate. Effective practise also requires keen listening. So we always teach with an ear toward the artistic goal.

We wish you and your students success in developing a refined technique and expressive artistry.

What is Technique?

The word **technique** (pronounced tek-NEEK) means **skill**.

What **technique** does a basketball player need?

Dribbling? Jumping? Shooting the ball?

What **technique** does a dancer need?

Balance? Graceful motion? Skilled leaps?

What **technique** does a pianist need?

Perfect posture? Fast fingers? Flexible wrists?

The exercises in this book will develop your piano technique.

Learn these five "technique secrets" with your teacher. Use them to begin your daily practice.

Five Secrets for Piano Technique

1. **The first secret is GOOD POSTURE.**

The "I'm Great" Pose

- Sit straight and tall on the front part of the stool. Centre your body to the **middle** of the keyboard.

- Check your **distance** from the keyboard by putting your arms straight in front of you with relaxed fists. **Your knuckles should touch the lid**. Adjust your stool as needed.

- Now place your hands in your lap. Take a deep breath and let it out.

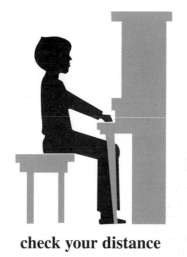 

check your distance   **good posture**

2. **The second secret is ROUND HAND SHAPE.**

Raise the Roof

- Rest your right hand (**R.H.**) lightly on the white keys in a loose fist.

- In s-l-o-w motion, let your fingers open to "raise the roof of your house." Your wrist will rise slightly as your fingertips and thumb hold your "house" in position.

- Repeat with the left hand (**L.H.**). Then try hands together (**H.T.**).

Lesson page 4 (Sitting at the Piano), page 5 (Making a Round Hand Shape)

3. The third secret is **FIRM FINGERTIPS.**

Making Glasses

- Gently press the tip of R.H. finger 2 against the tip of the thumb to make "glasses."

- Now do the same for fingers **1** and **3**, **1** and **4**, and **1** and **5**.

- Repeat using your L.H. fingers. Then try hands together.

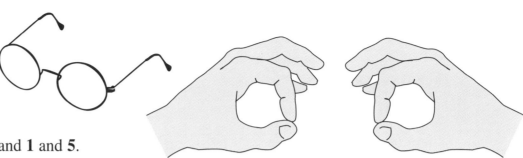

Look for a round shape.

4. The fourth secret is **ARM WEIGHT.**

Gorilla Arms

- Sitting at the piano, let your arms dangle straight down from your shoulders. *Pretend you have heavy gorilla arms!*

- In s-l-o-w m-o-t-i-o-n, bring your arms up. Your arms should continue to feel heavy. When your hands reach the height of the keyboard, let your arms drop *completely relaxed* into your lap.

- Do this exercise 2 times in slow motion.

5. The fifth secret is **CORRECT THUMB POSITION.**

Thumb Perch

The thumb should play on the **side tip** of the fingernail.

- Do a "thumb perch" by silently placing your right hand on the white keys with the thumb **"perching" on the side tip.** Your other fingers should rest gently on the keys.

- Then do a "thumb perch" with your left hand.

Note to Teacher: Finding the correct thumb position also eliminates a sagging wrist.

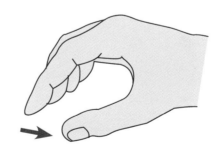

Lesson page 7 (Finger Flashcards), page 15 (The Old Clock), page 26 (C-D-E-F-G March)

Technique Secret:
firm fingertips (page 7)

Warm-up with *Making Glasses* for your **left hand**.

1. On the closed piano lid, silently play with **firm fingertips**. Say finger numbers aloud.

2. Next, play *softly* on the 3-black-keys with firm fingertips.

3. Repeat, playing with a *medium loud tone* (sound).

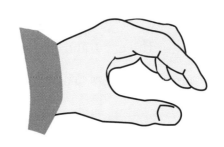

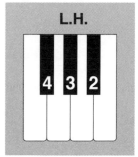

I Like Firm Fingertips
(for L.H. alone)

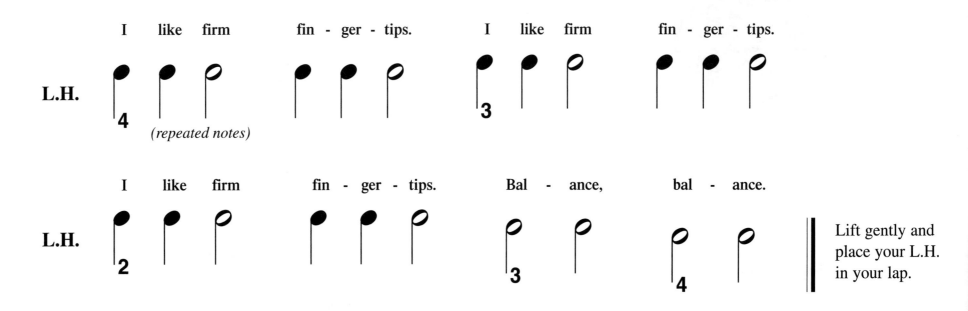

DISCOVERY Can you play *I Like Firm Fingertips* **by memory** on the LOWEST 3-black-key group?

Warm-up with *Making Glasses* for your **right hand**.

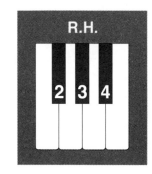

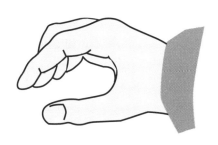

1. On the closed piano lid, silently play with **firm fingertips**.
   Say finger numbers aloud.

2. Next, play *softly* on the 3-black-keys with firm fingertips.

3. Repeat, playing with a *medium loud tone* (sound).

I Like Firm Fingertips
(for R.H. alone)

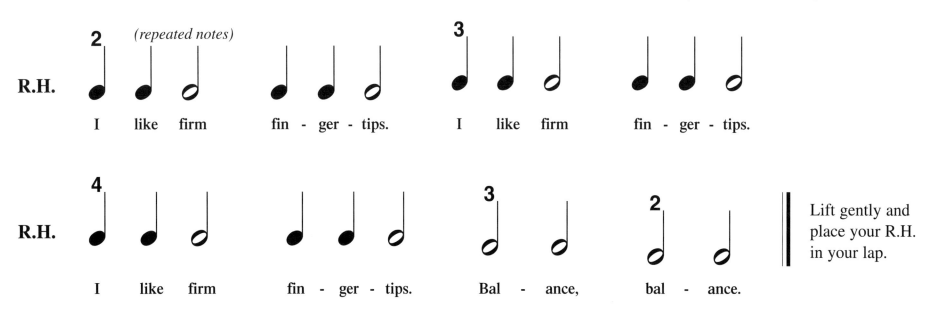

R.H.

2 *(repeated notes)*

I   like   firm   fin - ger - tips.

3

I   like   firm   fin - ger - tips.

R.H.

4

I   like   firm   fin - ger - tips.

3

Bal - ance,

2

bal - ance.

Lift gently and
place your R.H.
in your lap.

DISCOVERY   Can you play *I Like Firm Fingertips* hands together?

An **etude** (EH-tude) is a study piece.
• Say this word with your teacher.

This etude gives you practise playing **minims** with fingers 4 and 2.

Find the Keys

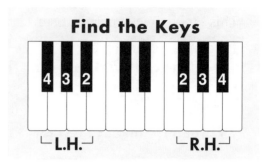

4 3 2 — L.H. — 2 3 4 — R.H. —

My First Etude

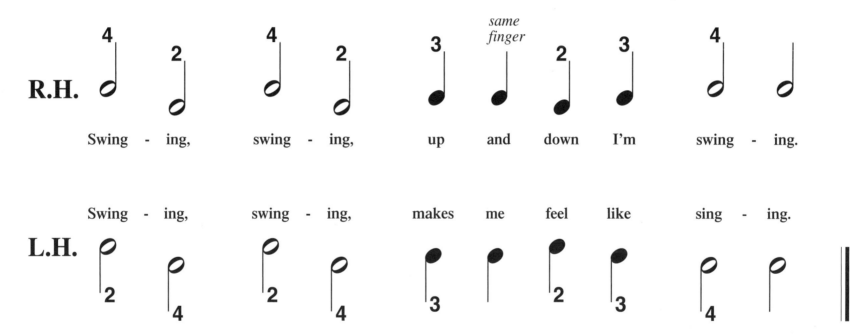

R.H.

4 2 4 2 3 *same finger* 2 3 4

Swing - ing,   swing - ing,   up   and   down   I'm   swing - ing.

Swing - ing,   swing - ing,   makes   me   feel   like   sing - ing.

L.H.

2 4 2 4 3 2 3 4

DISCOVERY Are you sitting tall and at the correct distance? Are you using a round hand shape? (see page 6)

Teacher Duet: (Student plays *high* on the keyboard)

R.H.

L.H.

p with pedal

This etude gives you practise:

1. counting semibreves
2. creating *forte* and *piano* sounds

• Circle the f and p signs in the music.

Find the Keys

Shepherd's Flute

Words by Crystal Bowman

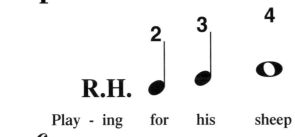

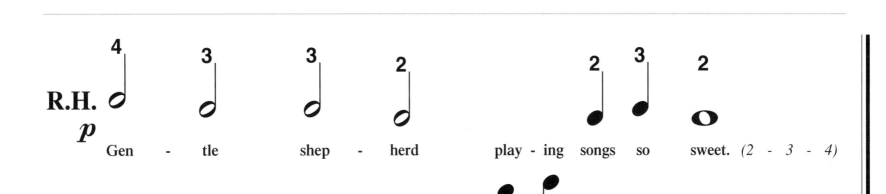

Play - ing   for   his   sheep *(2 - 3 - 4)*   as   they   go   to   sleep. *(2 - 3 - 4)*

Gen - tle   shep - herd   play - ing   songs   so   sweet. *(2 - 3 - 4)*

DISCOVERY You or your teacher may hold the pedal down for the entire song.
Can you find an echo in the piece?

Music becomes more beautiful when we play with expression or feeling.
Think of painting a musical picture!

1. First, circle all the f *(forte)* and p *(piano)* signs.

2. Now listen, creating **forte** and **piano** sounds as you play.

Find the Keys

L.H.   R.H.

All the Stars Are Shining

**You or your teacher may press the right-foot pedal
(sustain pedal) down throughout.**

*Repeat and
play softly!*

Start in the
MIDDLE
of the piano.

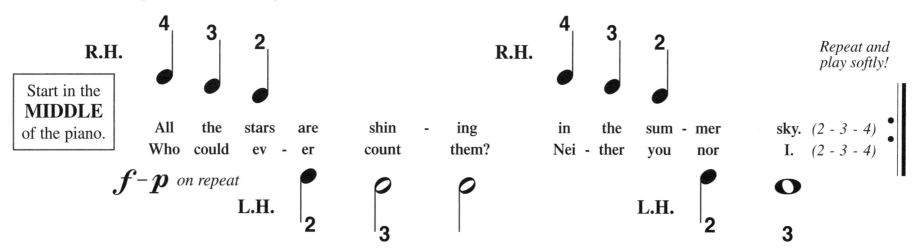

| All | the | stars | are | shin | - | ing | | in | the | sum - mer | | sky. *(2 - 3 - 4)* |
| Who | could | ev - er | | count | | them? | | Nei - ther | you | nor | | I. *(2 - 3 - 4)* |

f - p *on repeat*

Teacher Duet: (Student plays *high* on the keyboard)

mf - *pp* on repeat

Lesson pages 20-21 (Old MacDonald)

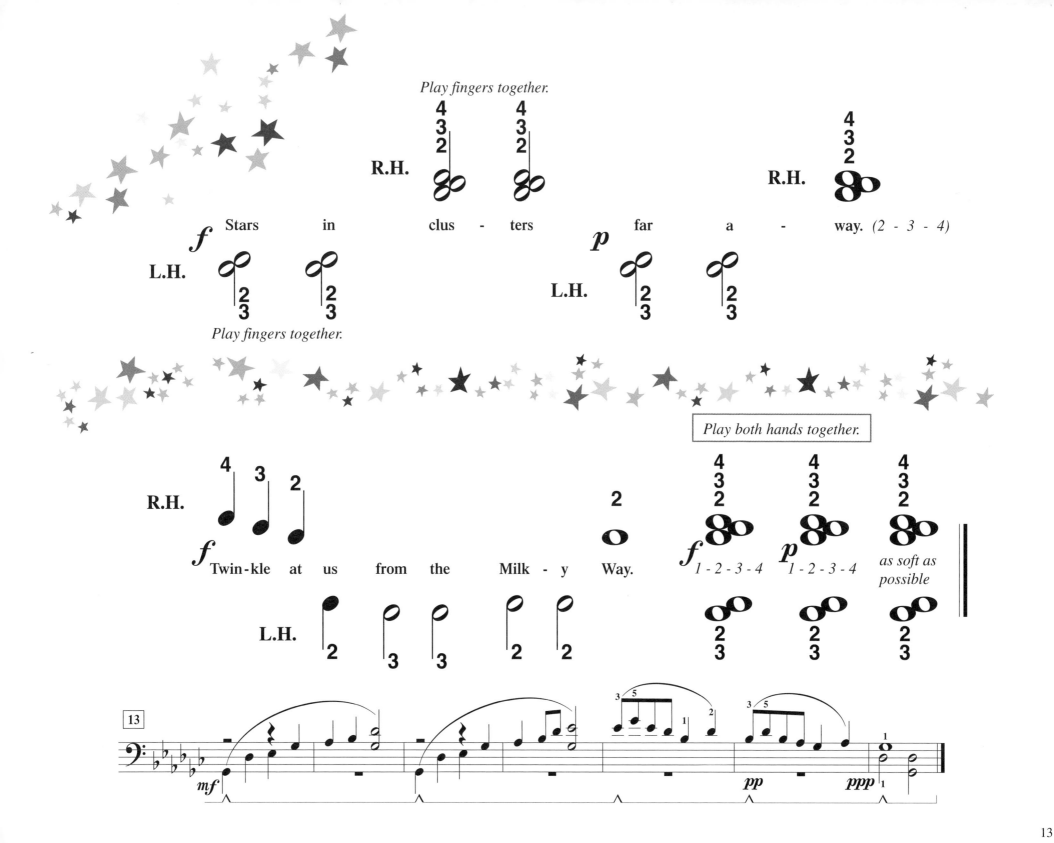

3 UNIT — CDEFGAB

Technique Secret:
firm fingertips (page 7)

Warm-up with *Making Glasses* for your **left hand**.

- For the first line, drop f into the keys.

- For the second line, gently play p for the *repeated* notes. Where do you return to f ?

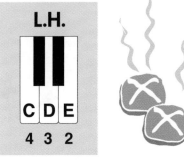

Hot Cross Buns
(for L.H. alone)

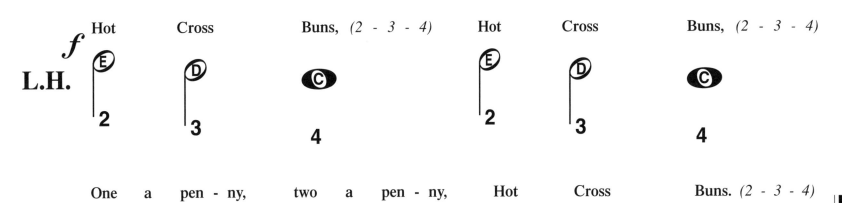

f L.H. — Hot (E) 2 — Cross (D) 3 — Buns, (2 - 3 - 4) C 4 — Hot (E) 2 — Cross (D) 3 — Buns, (2 - 3 - 4) C 4

p L.H. — One C a C pen - C ny, C 4 — two D a D pen - D ny, D — f Hot (E) — Cross (D) — Buns. (2 - 3 - 4) C

Teacher Duet: (Student plays *high* on the keyboard)

Technique Secret:
firm fingertips (page 7)

Warm-up with *Making Glasses* for your **right hand**.

R.H.

C D E

2 3 4

Hot Cross Buns
(for R.H. alone)

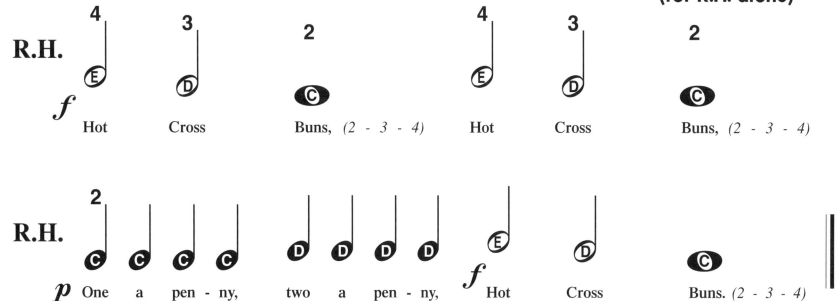

4 **3** **2** **4** **3** **2**

R.H. E D C E D C

f

Hot   Cross   Buns, *(2 - 3 - 4)*   Hot   Cross   Buns, *(2 - 3 - 4)*

2

R.H. C C C C D D D D E D C

p One a pen - ny, two a pen - ny, *f* Hot Cross Buns. *(2 - 3 - 4)*

DISCOVERY Can you play *Hot Cross Buns* hands together? Hint: Say the **letter names** aloud to help you.

Teacher Duet: (Student plays *high* on the keyboard)

Lesson page 24 (Merrily We Roll Along)   15

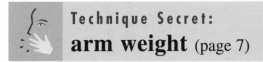

Technique Secret:
arm weight (page 7)

Warm-up with *Gorilla Arms* for your **left hand**.

Flying Saucer
(for L.H. alone)

1. Brace **L.H. finger 3** with the thumb.

2. Play the first line with only finger 3.

3. Repeat, using **L.H. fingers 5 - 4 - 3 - 2 - 1**. Use firm fingertips!

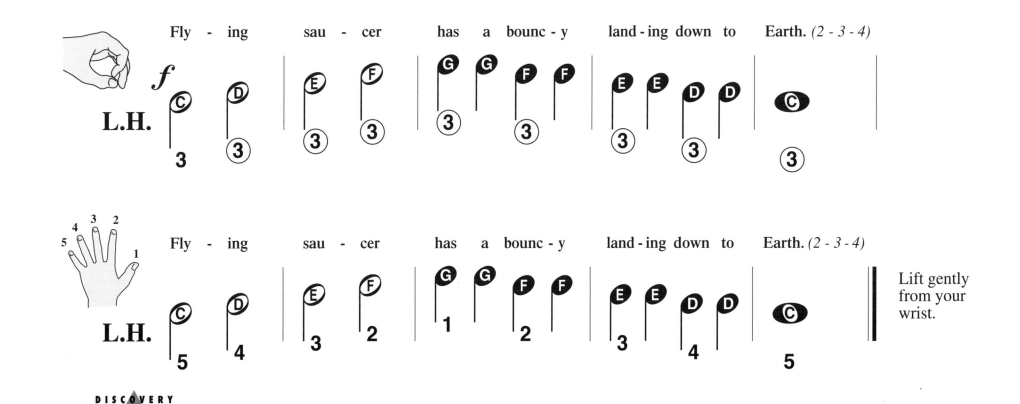

Fly - ing   sau - cer   has   a   bounc - y   land - ing down to   Earth. *(2 - 3 - 4)*

Lift gently
from your
wrist.

DISCOVERY Can you do STEP 3 above with your eyes closed?

Technique Secret:
arm weight (page 7)

Warm-up with *Gorilla Arms* for your **right hand**.

1. Brace **R.H. finger 3** with the thumb.

2. Play the first line with only finger 3.

3. Repeat, using **R.H. fingers 1 - 2 - 3 - 4 - 5**. Use firm fingertips!

Flying Saucer
(for R.H. alone)

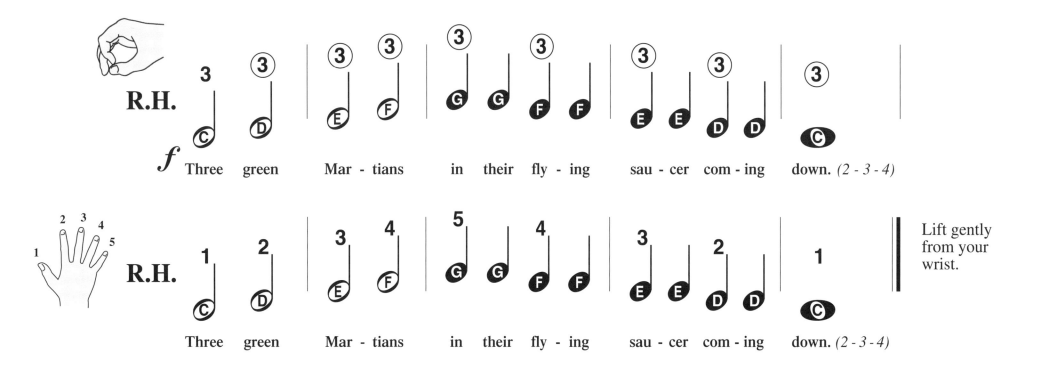

R.H.

f Three   green   Mar - tians   in   their   fly - ing   sau - cer   com - ing   down. *(2 - 3 - 4)*

R.H.

Three   green   Mar - tians   in   their   fly - ing   sau - cer   com - ing   down. *(2 - 3 - 4)*

Lift gently from your wrist.

DISCOVERY

Can you do STEP 3 above, playing both hands together?

Technique Secret:
correct thumb position (page 7)

Do a R.H. *Thumb Perch* as a daily warm-up.

This exercise uses all 5 fingers in a **musical pattern** that moves UP the keyboard.

1. First, tap the rhythm. Feel two beats for each minim.

2. Begin in the MIDDLE of the piano on a **C 5-finger scale**.

3. Begin and end each pattern with your thumb on the *side tip*.

A Fact About Beethoven
(for R.H. alone)

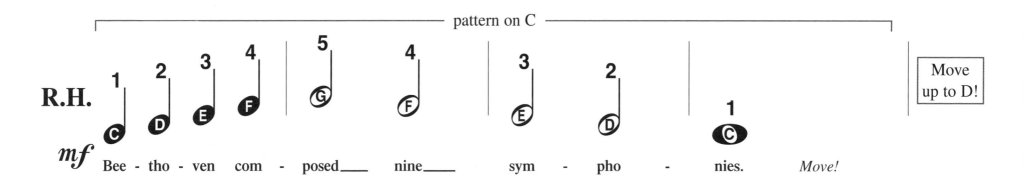

Teacher Duet: (Student plays *as written*)

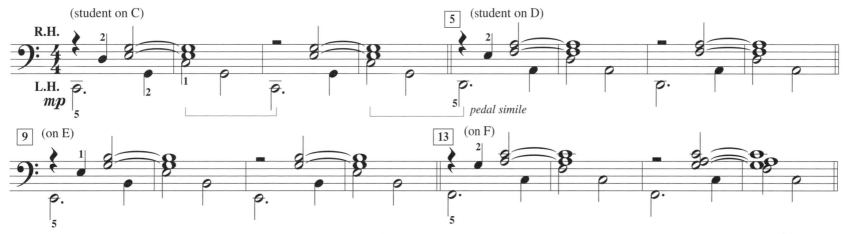

Note to Teacher: The student should not be required to play legato at this point.

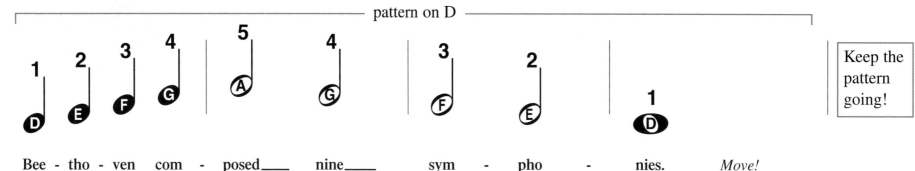

Keep the pattern going!

pattern on D

1 2 3 4 5 4 3 2 1
D E F G A G F E D

Bee - tho - ven com - posed____ nine____ sym - pho - nies. *Move!*

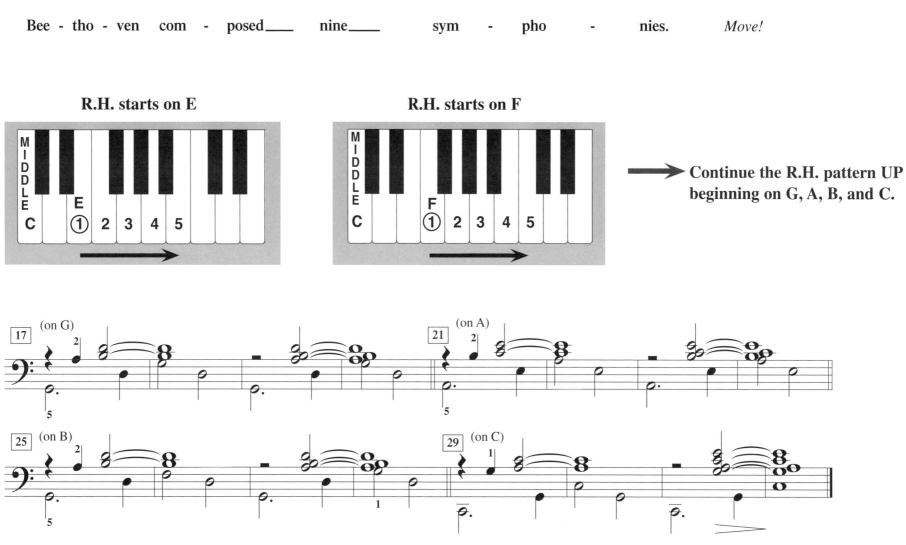

R.H. starts on E

R.H. starts on F

➡ **Continue the R.H. pattern UP beginning on G, A, B, and C.**

Technique Secret:
correct thumb position (page 7)

Do a L.H. *Thumb Perch* as a daily warm-up.

This exercise uses all 5 fingers in a **musical pattern** that moves DOWN the keyboard.

1. Start in the MIDDLE of the piano with your **left hand thumb on Middle C.**

2. Begin and end each pattern with your thumb on the *side tip*.

A Walk with Beethoven
(for L.H. alone)

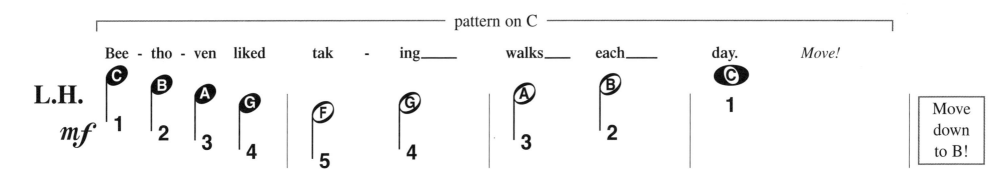

pattern on C

Bee - tho - ven liked tak - ing___ walks___ each___ day. *Move!*

L.H. *mf*

Move down to B!

Teacher Duet: (Student plays *as written***)**

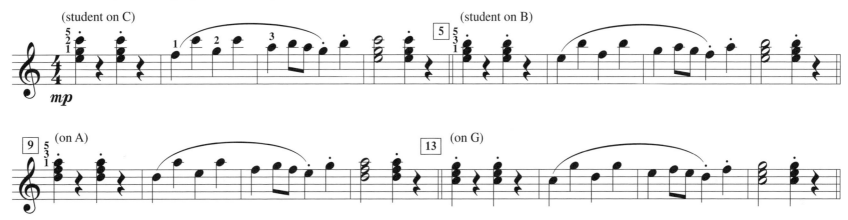

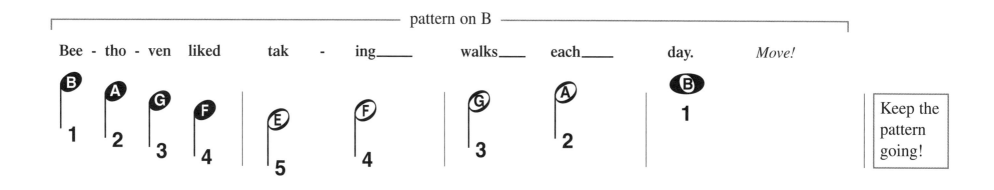

pattern on B

Bee - tho - ven liked tak - ing___ walks___ each___ day. *Move!*

Keep the pattern going!

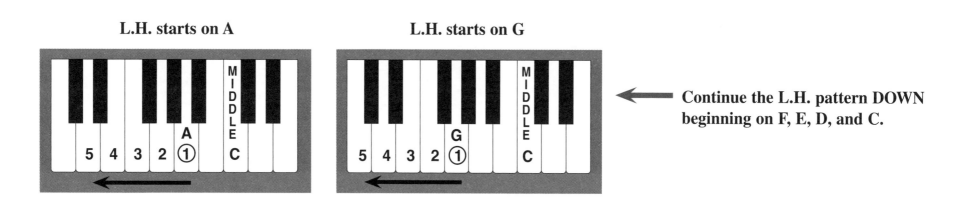

L.H. starts on A

L.H. starts on G

Continue the L.H. pattern DOWN beginning on F, E, D, and C.

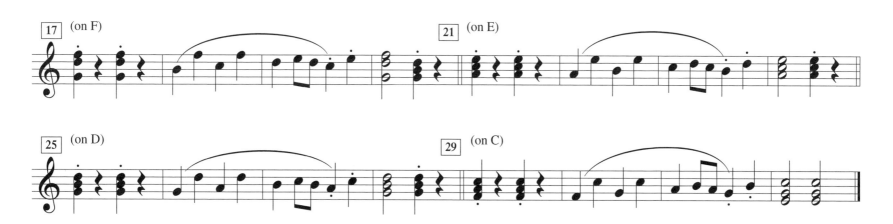

17 (on F)

21 (on E)

25 (on D)

29 (on C)

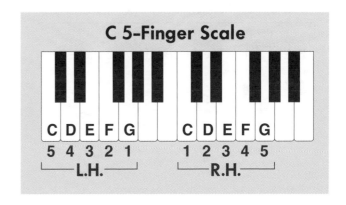

C 5-Finger Scale

Train's A-Comin'

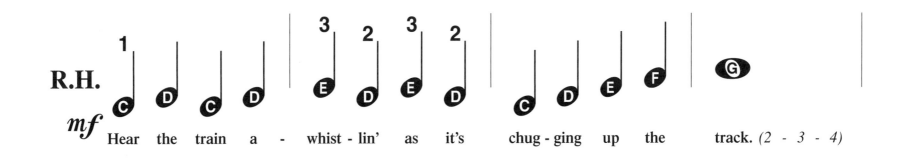

R.H.

mf

1   C   D   C   D   3 E   2 D   3 E   2 D   C   D   E   F   G

Hear the train a - whist - lin' as it's chug - ging up the track. *(2 - 3 - 4)*

Teacher Duet: (Student plays *high* on the piano)

R.H.

L.H.

mf

Lesson page 28 (Ode to Joy)

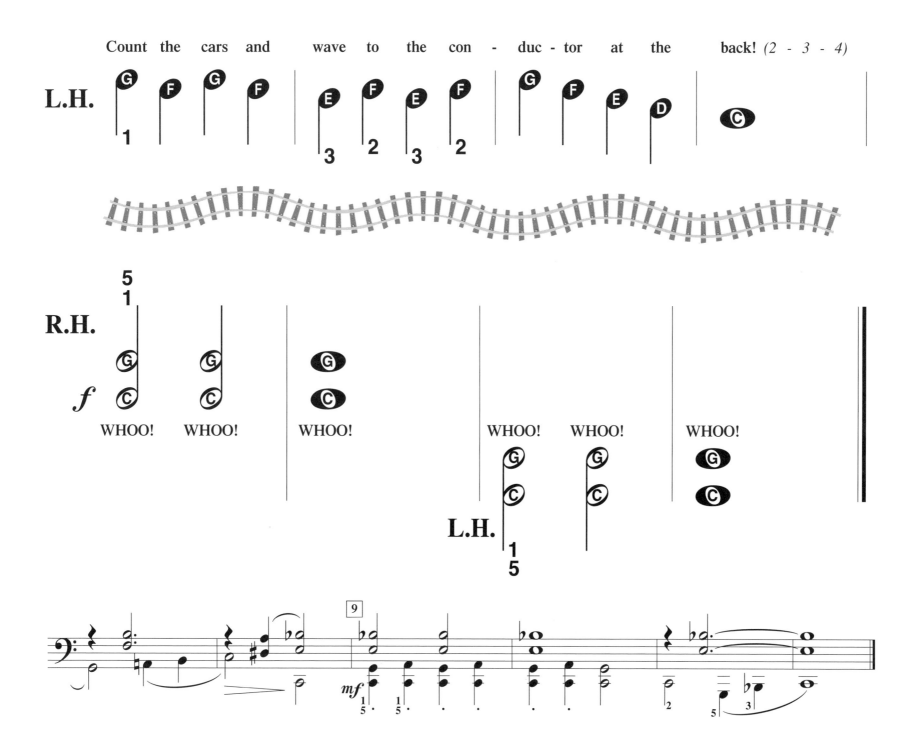

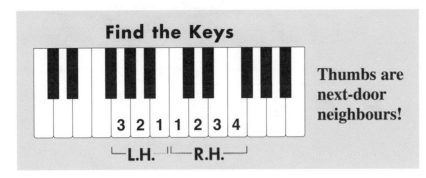

Find the Keys

3 2 1 1 2 3 4

L.H. R.H.

Thumbs are next-door neighbours!

A Song About Cats

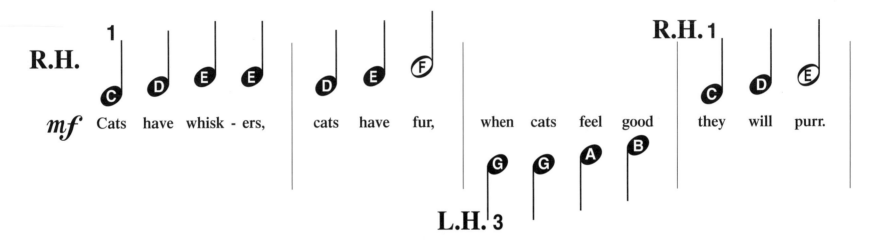

R.H.

1

C D E E | D E F | when cats feel good | R.H. 1 C D E

mf Cats have whisk - ers, cats have fur, they will purr.

G G A B

L.H. 3

Teacher Duet: (Student plays *high* on the piano)

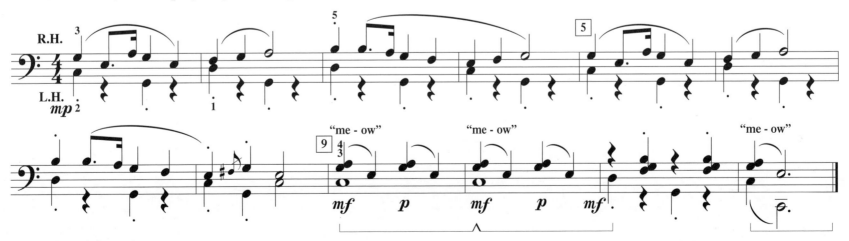

"me - ow"   "me - ow"   "me - ow"

24   Lesson page 31 (Alouette)

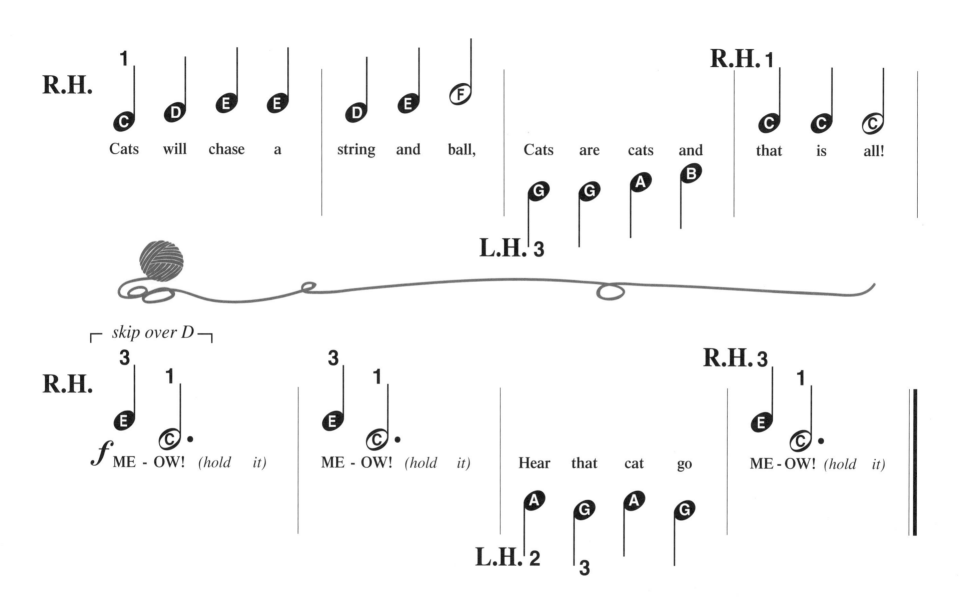

R.H.
1
C D E E | D E F |

Cats will chase a string and ball,

R.H. 1
C C C |

that is all!

Cats are cats and

L.H. 3
G G A B

⌐ *skip over D* ¬

R.H.
3 1
E C.

𝆑 ME - OW! *(hold it)*

3 1
E C.

ME - OW! *(hold it)*

Hear that cat go

R.H. 3 1
E C.

ME - OW! *(hold it)*

L.H. 2 3
A G A G

DISCOVERY

Can you hear the difference in your *mf* and 𝆑 sounds for this piece?

Technique Secret:
round hand shape (page 6)

Warm-up with *Raise the Roof* for your **right hand**.

Bicycle Bell
(for R.H. alone)

Your teacher will demonstrate these exercises.
• Can you make your bike move up quickly and smoothly?

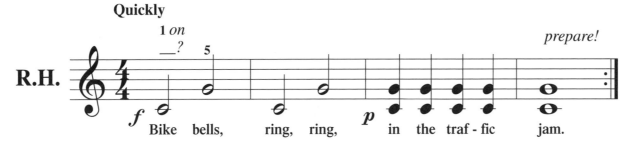

Play 3 TIMES.
Move to the next HIGHER C
for each repeat.

Big Blue Bus

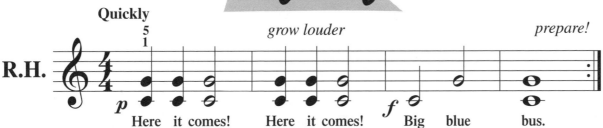

Play 3 TIMES.
Move to the next HIGHER C
for each repeat.

Technique Secret:

round hand shape (page 6)

Warm-up with *Raise the Roof* for your **left hand**.

Your teacher will demonstrate these exercises.

• Can you make your invention move down quickly and smoothly?

My Invention Works
(for L.H. alone)

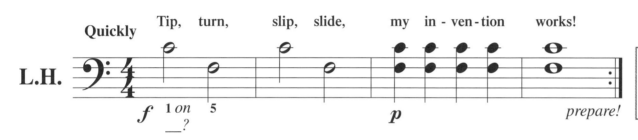

Tip, turn,   slip, slide,   my in - ven - tion   works!

L.H. Quickly

f 1 *on* 5
—?

p

prepare!

Play 3 TIMES.
Move to the next LOWER C
for each repeat.

My Robot Walks

Blink-ing light,   sil - ly sight,   ro - bot   walk!

L.H. Quickly

p 1
5

f

prepare!

Play 3 TIMES.
Move to the next LOWER C
for each repeat.

Technique Secret:
arm weight (page 7)

Warm-up with *Gorilla Arms* for both hands.

• Brace both finger 3s with the thumb. Drop with **arm weight** on beat 1 of each bar.

Dance Band Drummer

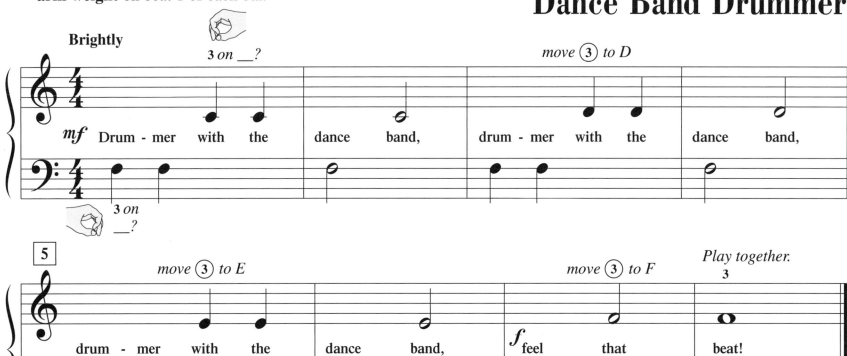

Brightly

3 on ___?

move ③ to D

mf   Drum - mer   with   the   dance   band,   drum - mer   with   the   dance   band,

3 on ___?

⑤   *move ③ to E*   *move ③ to F*   *Play together.*   3

drum - mer   with   the   dance   band,   f feel   that   beat!

3

Teacher Duet: (Student begins *1 octave higher*)

R.H.

L.H.

mp   mf

🎹 Lesson page 48 (The Dance Band)

This etude uses a musical pattern that "hops" up the keys.

The pattern changes from *f* to *p* as it moves up the keyboard.

1. First, play the entire exercise *p* to concentrate on "hops."

2. Play again and change from *f* to *p* for each pattern.

Hint: Play *close to the keys* with firm fingertips.

Frog and Turtle
(for R.H. alone)

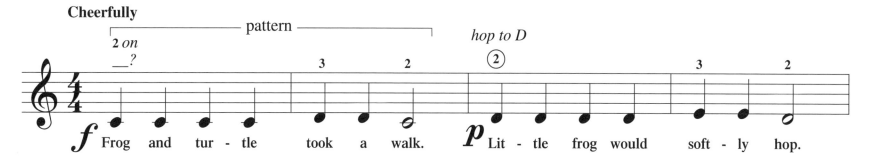

Cheerfully

pattern

2 on ___?

hop to D

f Frog and tur - tle took a walk. *p* Lit - tle frog would soft - ly hop.

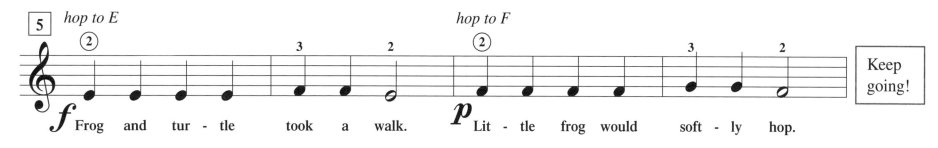

5 hop to E

hop to F

f Frog and tur - tle took a walk. *p* Lit - tle frog would soft - ly hop.

Keep going!

➤ **Continue this pattern UP beginning on G, A, B, and C, alternating *forte* and *piano*.**

How was your **technique**?
firm fingertips _____
rounded hand _____

How was your **sound**?
forte sounds _____
piano sounds _____

Lesson page 50 (Frogs on Logs)

Theme and Variations

Ferdinand Beyer
(1803–1863, Germany)
Op. 101

THEME
Cheerfully

1 on __?

— skip over E —

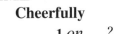

f   C   D   E   D   F   E   D   C

VARIATION 1
Cheerfully

mf   C   D   E   D

F   E   D   C

VARIATION 2

Cheerfully • Circle all the **repeated notes** in this variation.

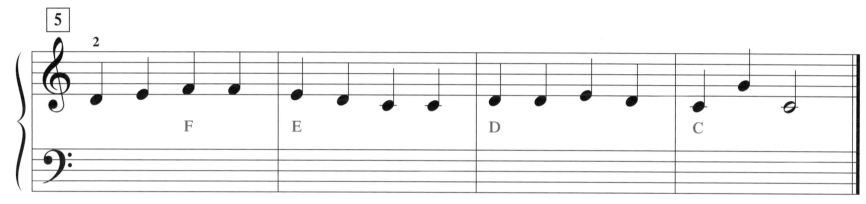

DISCOVERY

Can you play *Theme and Variations* with your **L.H. only** in the C 5-finger scale?

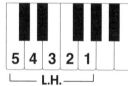

5 4 3 2 1
└── **L.H.** ──┘

Teacher Duet: (Student plays *1 octave higher*)

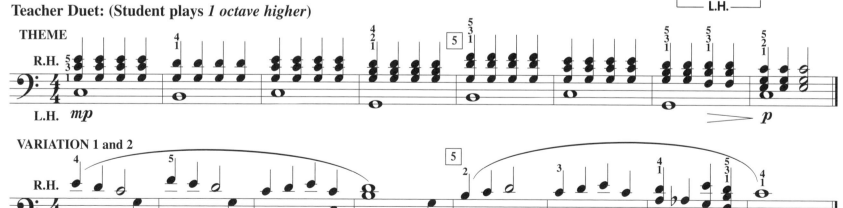

Technique Secret:
correct thumb position (page 7)

Do a L.H. *Thumb Perch* as a daily warm-up.

1. Notice this pattern begins and ends on the thumb.

2. When you can play this exercise easily, play it with eyes closed.

Carousel Ride
(for L.H. alone)

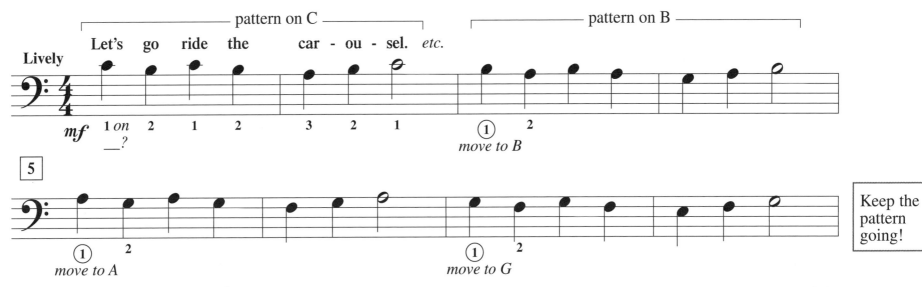

Keep the pattern going!

⬅ **Continue the 1 - 2 - 1 - 2 - 3 - 2 - 1 pattern DOWN beginning on F, E, D, and C.**

Teacher Duet: (Student plays *as written*)

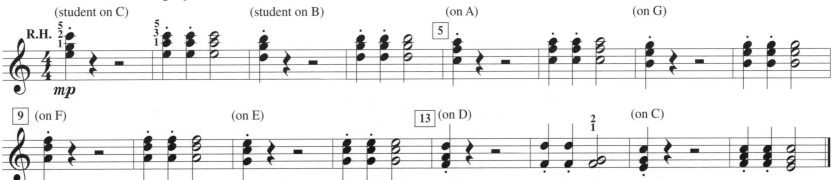

ETUDE

In this etude, one hand moves higher while the other hand is still playing!

1. First, find your starting position and *silently* practise the hand shifts.

2. Now play s-l-o-w-l-y, with your right hand preparing ahead.
   Gradually work up to a lively speed.

Two Squirrels Chasing

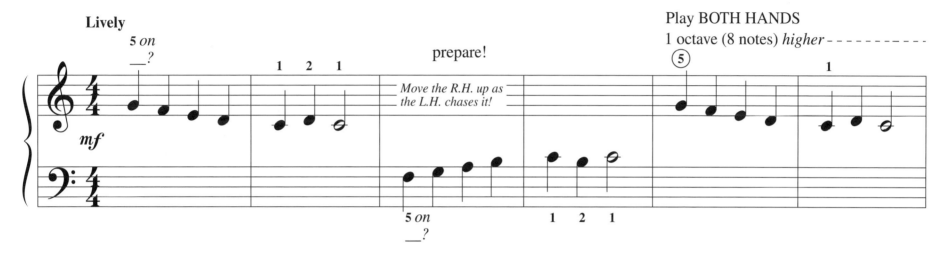

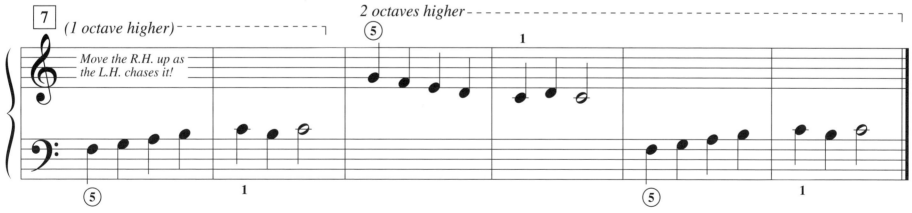

 How was your **preparation**?

Lesson page 57 (The Birch Tree)   33

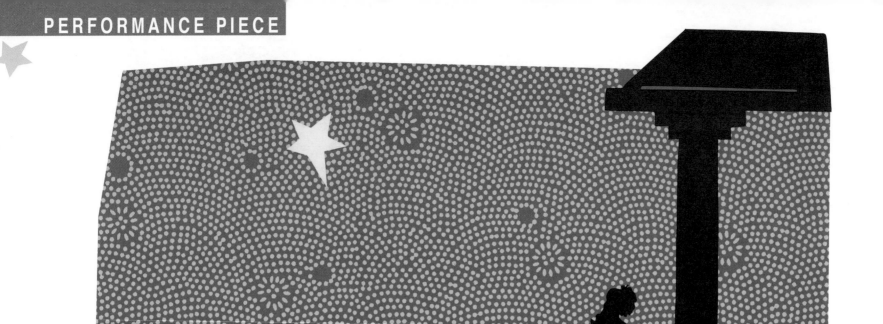

Twinkle, Twinkle Little Star

• Circle all the **repeated notes**.

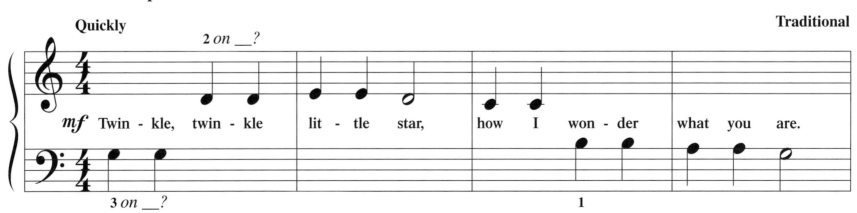

Quickly

Traditional

2 on __?

mf Twin - kle, twin - kle | lit - tle star, | how I won - der | what you are.

3 on __?

1

Optional: For solo, play BOTH HANDS
1 octave (8 notes) higher from *bar 7*
to the end. Your teacher will show you how.

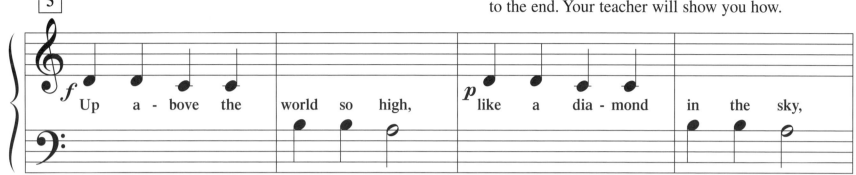

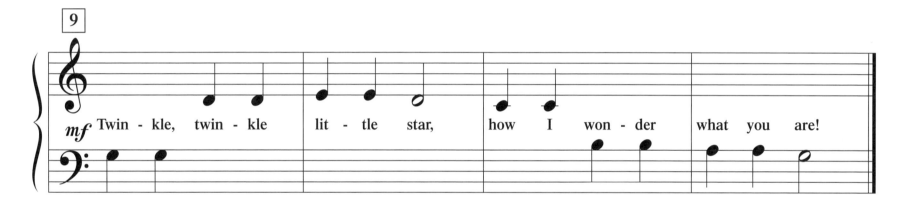

DISCOVERY

Where is there an echo in this piece? Show your teacher.

Teacher Duet: (Student plays *as written*)

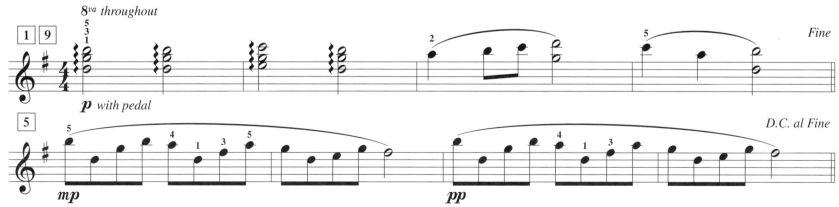

35

Technique Secret:
round hand shape (page 6)

Warm-up with *Raise the Roof* for your **right hand**.

1. Notice this 2-bar pattern **skips** and then **steps**.

2. When you can play this exercise easily, play it with your eyes closed.
   Remember to play your thumb on the *side tip*.

Baby Elephant
(for R.H. alone)

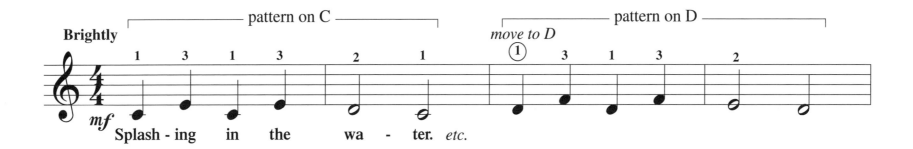

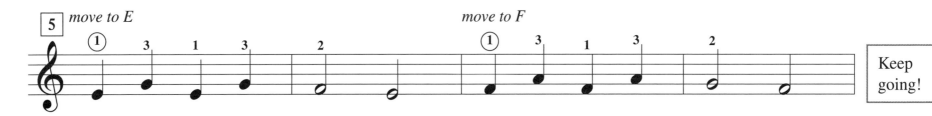

Keep going!

➡ **Continue the 1 - 3 - 1 - 3 - 2 - 1 pattern UP beginning on G, A, B, and C.**

DISCOVERY
Repeat this exercise using this finger pattern: **2 - 4 - 2 - 4 - 3 - 2.**

Warm-up with *Raise the Roof* for your **left hand**.

1. Now practise the same finger pattern for your left hand.

2. When you can play this exercise easily, play it with your eyes closed. Remember to play on the *side tip* of the thumb.

Mother Elephant
(for L.H. alone)

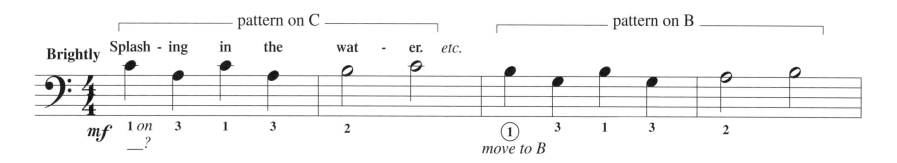

pattern on C   pattern on B

Brightly   Splash - ing   in   the   wat - er. *etc.*

mf   1 *on*   3   1   3   2   ①   3   1   3   2
     __?

move to B

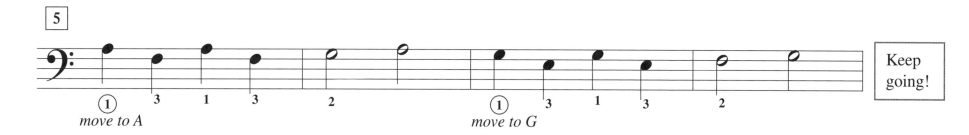

5

①   3   1   3   2   ①   3   1   3   2

move to A   *move to G*

Keep going!

← **Continue the 1 - 3 - 1 - 3 - 2 - 1 pattern DOWN beginning on F, E, D, and C.**

DISCOVERY   Repeat this exercise using this finger pattern: **2 - 4 - 2 - 4 - 3 - 2.**

A good pianist does not hesitate at the bar line.

Practise *bars 5–8* with a flowing motion that moves over the bar line.

Etude Check:

___ 1. Are you creating **forte**, **mezzo forte**, and **piano** sounds?

___ 2. Is your rhythm flowing over the bar line? (no hesitations)

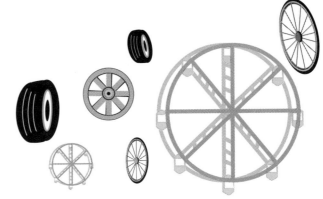

Optional: Hold the right-foot pedal (sustain pedal) down throughout the piece.

Wheels Going 'Round

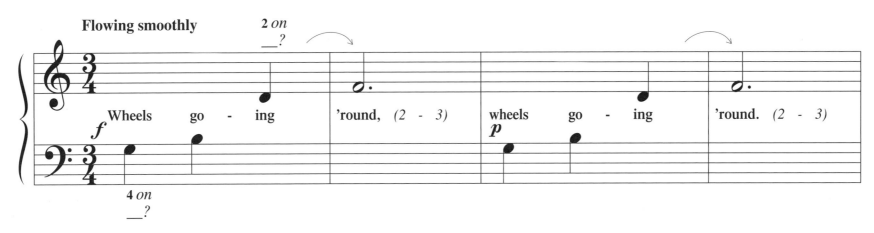

Teacher Duet: (Student plays *1 octave higher*)

Lesson page 66 (Happy Day!)

Dancing with Frankenstein

Dancing merrily

Frank - en - stein,   Frank - en - stein,   he's   in   a   trance, *(2 - 3)*

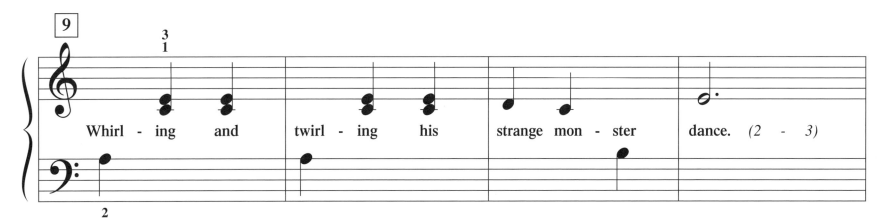

Whirl - ing   and   twirl - ing   his   strange mon - ster   dance. *(2 - 3)*

Teacher Duet: (Student plays *1 octave higher*)

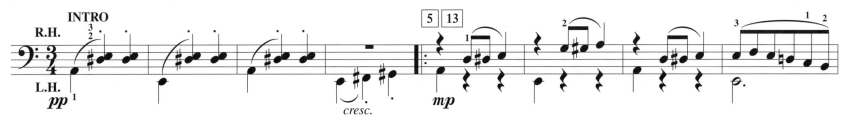

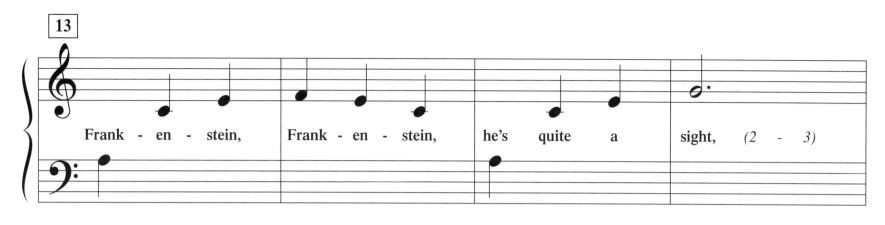

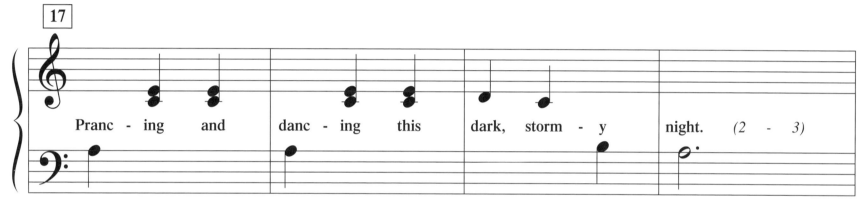

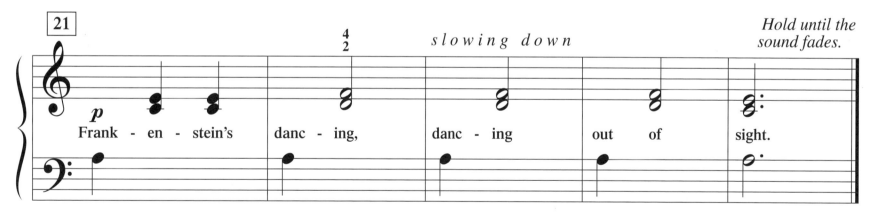

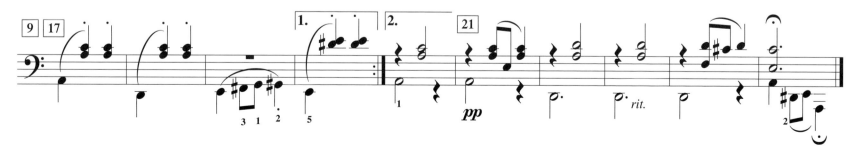

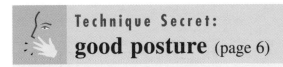

Technique Secret:
good posture (page 6)

Warm-up with *The "I'm Great" Pose*.

1. *Memorise* this skipping pattern.

2. Watch each hand as you play to keep a round hand position.

Kitten on the Keys

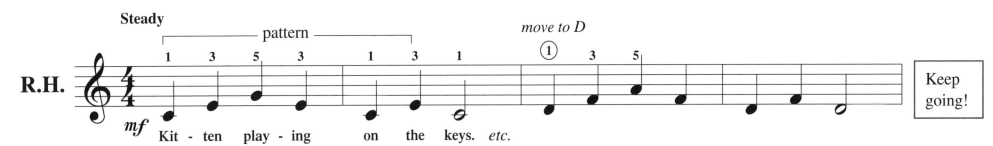

Continue this pattern UP beginning on E, F, G, A, B, and C.

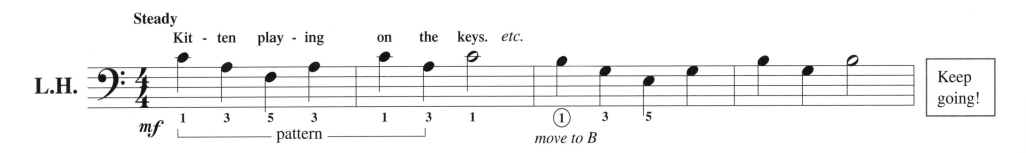

Continue this pattern DOWN beginning on A, G, F, E, D, and C.

Mr. Köhler's Etude

Louis Köhler
(1820-1886, Germany)
Op. 300

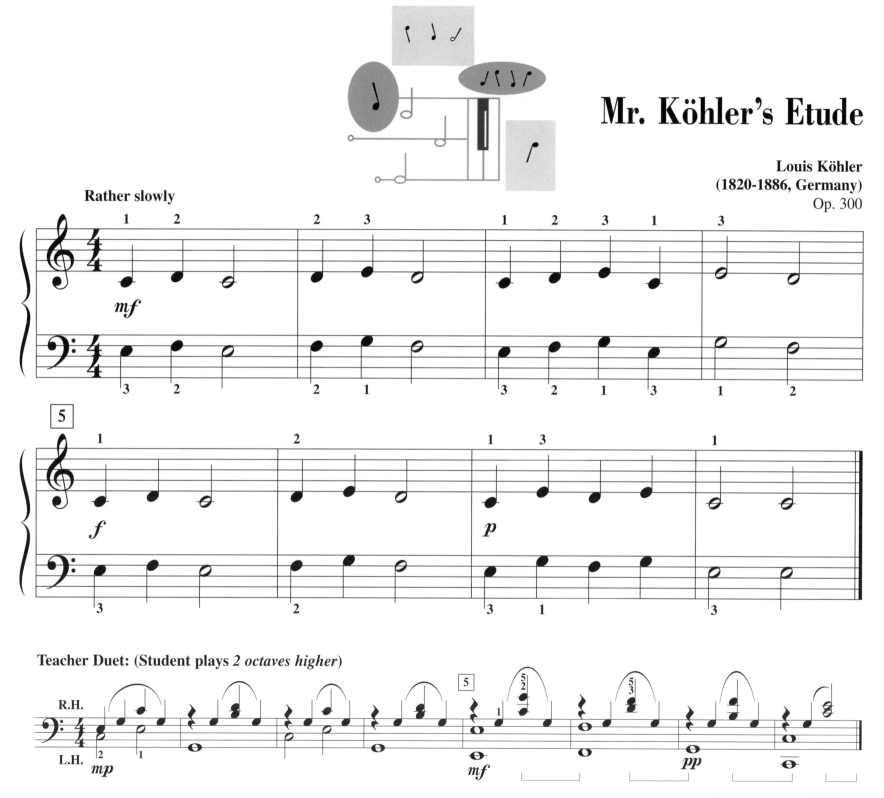

Teacher Duet: (Student plays *2 octaves higher*)

Horseback Riding

_____ 5-Finger Scale

Galloping along

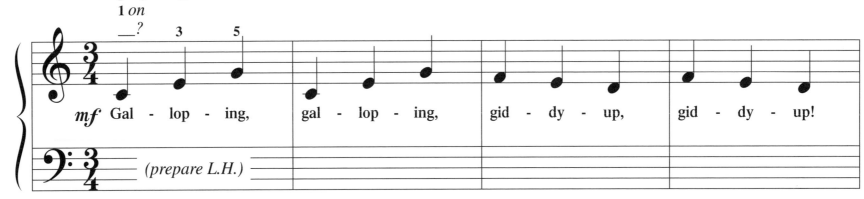

Gal - lop - ing, gal - lop - ing, gid - dy - up, gid - dy - up!

(prepare L.H.)

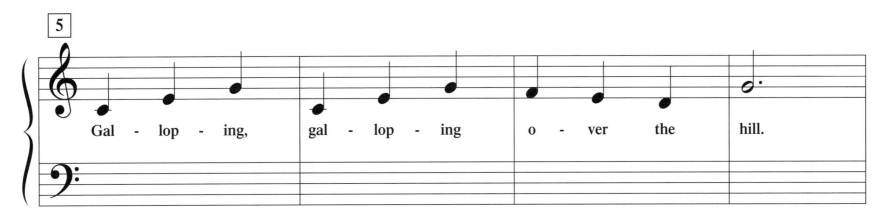

Gal - lop - ing, gal - lop - ing o - ver the hill.

Teacher Duet: (Student plays _1 octave higher_)

44 Lesson page 73 (Musical Question and Answer)

DISCOVERY Circle the **time signature**. Tap this piece, counting aloud "1 - 2 - 3." Be sure to tap with the correct hand!

Technique Secret:
you be the teacher

Can you name and demonstrate for your teacher
3 out of the 5 "technique secrets"? (See pages 6-7)

1. _____

2. _____

3. _____

Let's Ride Bikes!

With energy

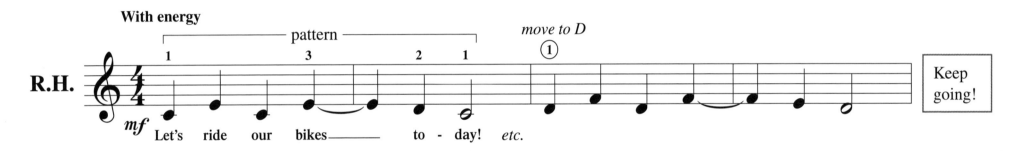

Let's ride our bikes——— to - day! *etc.*

→ **Continue this pattern UP beginning on E, F, G, A, B, and C.**

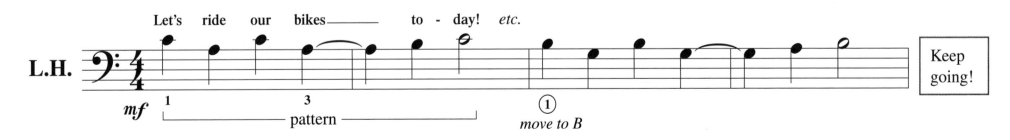

Let's ride our bikes——— to - day! *etc.*

← **Continue this pattern DOWN beginning on A, G, F, E, D, and C.**

DISCOVERY Play *Let's Ride Bikes!* using **fingers 2-3-4**.

A fine pianist can play one hand *forte* and the other hand *piano*.

1. Before playing, say the name of each **dynamic mark** in the piece.

2. Now play and listen for *forte, mezzo forte,* and *piano* sounds!

• Use a braced R.H. finger 3 for line 1.

• Open the hand to play line 2.

Peaceful Sunset

Hold the right-foot pedal (sustain pedal) down throughout.

Teacher Duet: (Student plays *1 octave higher*)

Lesson page 79 (Bells of Great Britain)

Trumpet Song

_____ 5-Finger Scale

Reading Check:
Circle each **skip** in this piece.
Hint: There are 8.

Jeremiah Clarke
(1673–1707, England)
arranged

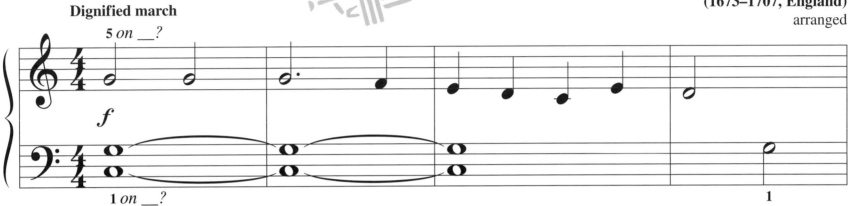

Teacher Duet: (Student plays *2 octaves higher*)

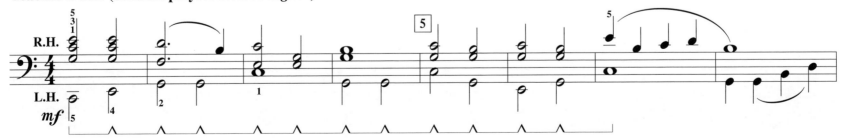

Lesson page 79 (Bells of Great Britain)

DISCOVERY As your teacher plays the solo, can you clap only on **beat 1 of each bar**?
Hint: Count aloud **1** - 2 - 3 - 4 to help you feel the beat.

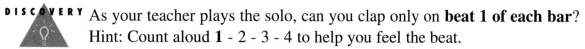

Technique Secret:
you be the teacher

Can you name and show your teacher all five "technique secrets"? (See pages 6-7)

1. _____

2. _____

3. _____

4. _____

5. _____

Hand Clap Game

📖 Lesson page 83 (Princess or Monster?)

Tai Chi is a gentle movement activity that helps flexibility and balance.

- Play this etude slowly. Keep your hands relaxed but fingertips firm.

- Notice the L.H. will shift at *bar 5*.

Morning Tai Chi

Gentle and flowing

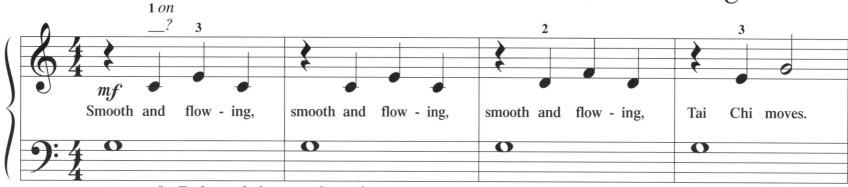

3 on __? Feel your balance on finger 3.

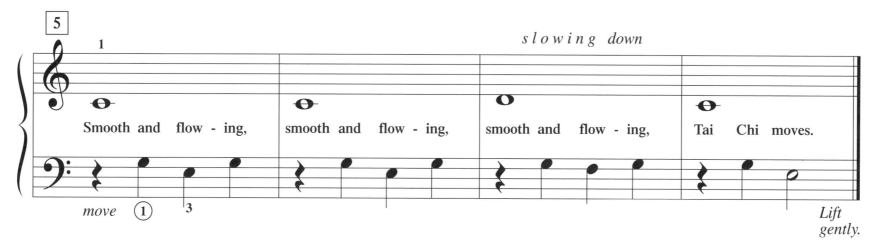

Teacher Duet: (Student plays *as written*)

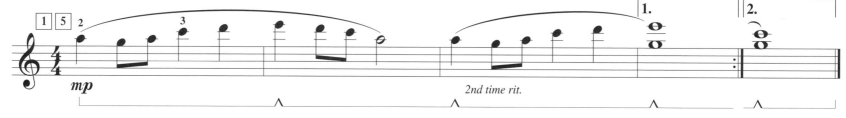

Lesson page 83 (Princess or Monster?)

Rain, Rain, Go Away

5-Finger Scale

Moderately fast

mf Rain, rain, go a - way, come a - gain an - o - ther day.

Teacher Duet: (Student plays *1 octave higher*)

Lesson pages 84-85 (The Bugle Boys)

Sun, sun, shine to - day, let me go and play!

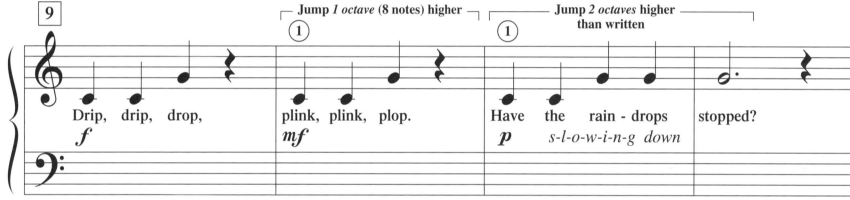

Jump *1 octave* (8 notes) higher

Jump *2 octaves* higher
than written

Drip, drip, drop, *f* plink, plink, plop. *mf* Have the rain - drops *p* *s-l-o-w-i-n-g down* stopped?

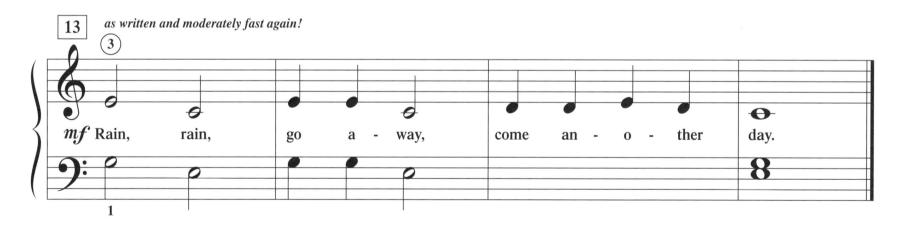

as written and moderately fast again!

mf Rain, rain, go a - way, come an - o - ther day.

DISCOVERY  Circle the three **crotchet rests** in this piece.

A Grand Celebration

Ferdinand Beyer
(1803-1863, Germany)
Op. 101, No. 9

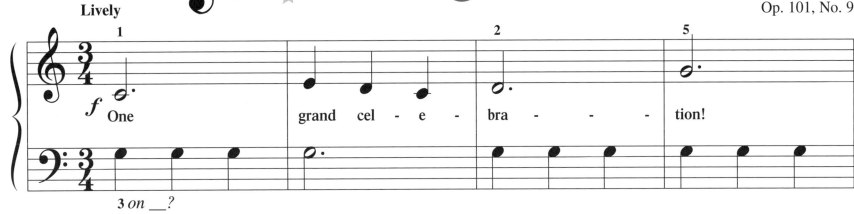

Lively

One — grand cel - e - bra - - - tion!

3 *on* __?

It's — my grad - u - a - - - tion. Let's have

Teacher Duet: (Student plays *1 octave higher*)

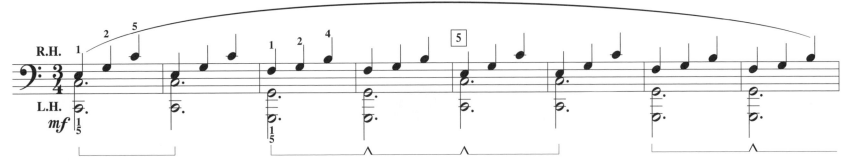

R.H.

L.H.

mf

Lesson pages 84-85 (The Bugle Boys)

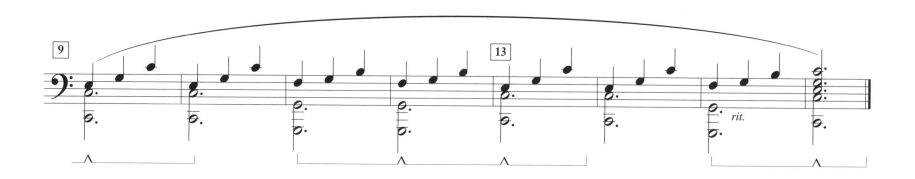

Piano Adventures® Certificate

Congratulations to:

_____

(Your Name)

You have completed the PRIMER LEVEL and are now ready for LEVEL 1

**LESSON
& THEORY**　　　　　**TECHNIQUE
& PERFORMANCE**

Teacher:_____

Date:_____